BOOK TEN

FOURWAYS FARM

Three of a Kind

SIMON & SCHUSTER
YOUNG BOOKS
IN ASSOCIATION WITH CHANNEL FOUR TELEVISION.

Available from all good bookshops.

For further information on the series, write to:
The Marketing Department,
Simon & Schuster Young Books,
Campus 400, Maylands Avenue,
Hemel Hempstead,
Herts HP2 7EZ

Trio Uno Duo

Brenda

Ginger

Davenport

FOURWAYS FARM

Three of a Kind

Dudley　　　　　Martha　　　　　Godfrey

Text adapted from the scripts of Chris Ellis
based on an original idea by Tom Stanier.

Science Adviser: Malcolm Ward
Science Notes: Sally Nankivell-Aston
Design: Between the Lines
Illustrations: Tessa Richardson-Jones based on
puppets by Alan Platt and
sets by Max Stewart.

The television programmes on which this work
is based were produced for Channel Four Television
and Nederlandse Onderwijs Televisie
by Case Television Limited.

First published in Great Britain in 1994 by
Simon & Schuster Young Books, Campus 400, Maylands
Avenue, Hemel Hempstead, Herts HP2 7EZ.

British Library Cataloguing in Publications Data available.
ISBN: 0 7500 1645 0

I can see a thing or two from my high perch up above Fourways Farm. There's always something interesting going on down there. Right now Brenda is in a party mood, but she won't tell the other animals why.

"What are we celebrating?" Trio asked.

"Just wait and see," said Brenda. "But I can tell you one thing – I'm expecting special guests."

"How many?" asked Trio.

6

"Something tells me there will be three," smiled Brenda. "Three different ones – but three of a kind," she added, mysteriously.

The animals were puzzled.

"I bet it's us," said Dudley to Martha and Davenport.
"Why?" asked Martha.
"Because we've all got four legs," answered Dudley.

"So have lots of other animals on the farm," said Ginger. "It's got to be something special about just three animals."

9

"It's us, it's us!" cried the rats, excitedly. "We're three of a kind."

"Yes, you are three of the same kind of animal," said Brenda. "But you're not my three special guests."

"I've got it!" barked Davenport.

"It's all the 'Ds' – Dudley, Duo and Davenport. We're the three special guests."
"No," quacked Brenda.

"Then it's got to be the three females," purred Ginger. "Martha, Brenda and me!"

"No, but you're getting close," said Brenda. "I'll tell you."

Brenda waddled off her nest and showed everyone what she had been sitting on.

"My eggs," she said, proudly. "My three special guests."

"Oh, is that all you have to do to have eggs – just sit around?" asked Dudley.

"You have to be female," Brenda explained.

"Could *I* have one?" Martha asked.

"Somehow I don't think cows lay eggs," said Brenda.

Brenda's eggs soon hatched out and they were exactly as she had said – three of a kind.

"Ah . . . cute little things," sighed Dudley.

15

"Come along, follow me!" said Brenda to her little ones.
"We're off for a swim."

After the ducklings' first swim, it was party time.
"Take your places," called Brenda.

18

"I say," said Davenport. "Where are the rats? They may be troublemakers, but we can't have the party without them."

"Hang on! Wait for us!" called Duo.

"Every party should have a surprise," said Uno. "And if
Brenda can hatch her ducklings, we rats can hatch a . . .
RATLING!!"

That night the animals snuggled up in the barn. They were all different, in all sorts of ways. But there was one thing they had in common – they all got on with each other. Well, *most* of the time!

"Is it just birds that lay eggs?" asked Godfrey.
"I wonder . . . " said Martha.

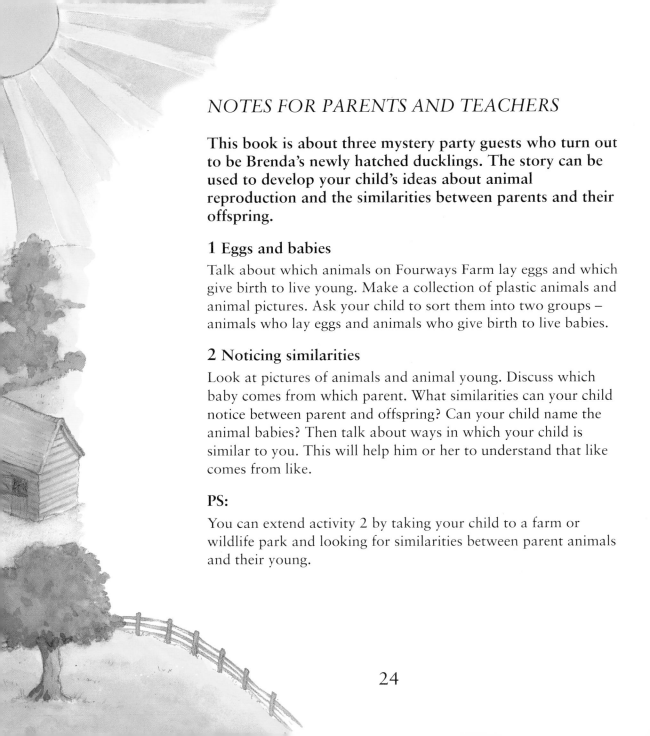

NOTES FOR PARENTS AND TEACHERS

This book is about three mystery party guests who turn out to be Brenda's newly hatched ducklings. The story can be used to develop your child's ideas about animal reproduction and the similarities between parents and their offspring.

1 Eggs and babies

Talk about which animals on Fourways Farm lay eggs and which give birth to live young. Make a collection of plastic animals and animal pictures. Ask your child to sort them into two groups – animals who lay eggs and animals who give birth to live babies.

2 Noticing similarities

Look at pictures of animals and animal young. Discuss which baby comes from which parent. What similarities can your child notice between parent and offspring? Can your child name the animal babies? Then talk about ways in which your child is similar to you. This will help him or her to understand that like comes from like.

PS:

You can extend activity 2 by taking your child to a farm or wildlife park and looking for similarities between parent animals and their young.